SWEET IS MY SWAGGER

JoJo Siwa: Be Happy Journal
A CENTUM BOOK 978-1-912396-56-6
Published in Great Britain by Centum Books Ltd
This edition published 2018
1 3 5 7 9 10 8 6 4 2

Centum Books Ltd, 20 Devon Square,
Newton Abbot, Devon, TQ12 2HR, UK

books@centumbooksltd.co.uk

CENTUM BOOKS Limited Reg. No. 07641486

A CIP catalogue record for this book is
available from the British Library

Printed in Italy

centum

Contents

There's so much fun inside, including:

Super Cute

DREAM Crazy BIG

BE YOU

7

Be positive, be you!

Everyone has something that makes them unique and special. Read about JoJo's top five traits, then think about the things that make you special and write them down opposite.

1. JoJo's positive attitude really shines through. Have you ever seen her frown?

2. She's not afraid of hard work and getting the job done, after all, girls never quit.

3. JoJo loves bows; they are her signature style. Bows make everything better!

HAPPY THOUGHTS

4. JoJo has a voice and she's not afraid to use it. Whether it's vlogging or singing, she's got star power.

5. JoJo always tries to be herself and not let the haters get her down. #EVER!

SWEET

1. I'm they only person in my family who can do ~~GMA~~ Gymnastic

2. I have such a cute baby cousin

3.

BE YOU

4.

5.

Super Cute

9

Awesome cloud

JoJo has written down some her favourite things in the cloud. Fill in your cloud opposite with your favourite things — use doodles or words!

Singing

My BFFs

Dancing

Bows

Family

Fans

BOW Bow

Your favourite things can be anything you like. Think about all the awesome things you love to do, visit, eat and play with and add them to your cloud.

My life

Use this page to write about what you do on a typical day each week.

★★★★	morning	afternoon	evening
Monday			Gym
Tuesday	PE, Homework ↓		Swimming bath
Wednesday			
Thursday			
Friday	Lust day of SALS		
Saturday			
Sunday			bath

Wake up at:

School starts at:

Eat lunch at:

Finish school:

Eat dinner at:

Go to sleep at:

DID YOU KNOW JOJO LOVES VEGGIES — ESPECIALLY SALADS!

EAT DANCE SLEEP

Family tree

Fill in your family tree with names, pics or doodles to show who's who in your family.

Who is the cuddliest?

...............Flo...............

Who is the loudest?

...............Me...............

Who is the happiest?

...............Florence rose...............

Who is the messiest?

Peter Flo and William

Who is the funniest?

Me

Who is the chattiest?

Me

Who is the cutest?

Me and Flo

SWEET

Who is the smartest?

Me

BFFs

Which of your pals is your

best mate: Sienna Jess.L Alice Isabelle JessP Alex Elizabeth Edward

kindest pal: Jess.L Me, Alice

funniest friend: Me

oldest friend: Alice Jessica

Which of your friends is the

best dancer:

Me

most organised:

Me

best shopper:

Me

most scatterbrained:

P Rose (me)

WHO IS MOST LIKE
JOJO IN YOUR
FRIENDSHIP GROUP?

Selfie style

JoJo is always behind the camera, whether it's shooting a new video, making a new vlog or taking a selfie for her socials. Discover her top tips for vlogging and selfies!

1. Clean the lens on your phone or camera – you don't want to appear misty to your audience!

2. Make sure to take pictures in good light. If you can't see something, then the camera won't either.

3. Reflections are bad so avoid shiny windows, mirrors and plastic surfaces.

4. It's good to focus on one thing for maximum impact, so make sure that you or your subject appears front and centre in your shots.

5. Keep your background free from mess for crisp, clean shots – this might mean that you have to tidy your bedroom!

6. Don't use your flash – only if it's super essential. Natural light is WAY more pleasing to the eye.

7. Frame your shot, guys! Think of your screen as a cross-section of lines, something like this:

8. Use a backdrop when shooting objects or poses to make things really stand out. A white wall can work really well and it's so simple.

9. Learn to edit your videos and photos. There's so much info online (including vlogs) to help you get started. Make your pieces pop with fun graphics and editing tools!

10. Don't forget to smile and be confident. Speak clearly in vlogs and project your voice like a true pro.

Friendship *quiz*

1. When did you and your BFF first meet?

- A   I remember it like it was yesterday
- B   School I think ✓
- C   Ummm, next question?

2. What is your favourite thing to do with your BFF?

- A   Talk for hours and hours and hours ✓
- B   We just like to hang out now and again
- C   I don't really have a favourite thing

3. What's her favourite food?

- A   Anything that we can share together ✓
- B   I'm going to guess pizza
- C   Is it school lunches?

4. What are you getting your friend for their birthday?

- A   Something they've wanted for ages! ✓
- B   Maybe a shop gift card?
- C   I'll probably just get them something the day before

5. What's your favourite thing about your BFF?

    A   Everything! I can't name one thing.

    B   They're cool, like me ✓

    C   Not sure

6. Have you seen your BFF cry?

    A   Yes, especially at soppy films!

    B   Not really, we're not close like that ✓

    C   No way!

7. Has your BFF met your family?

    A   Yeah, we're always hanging out at each others' houses

    B   Maybe once or twice ✓

    C   No, they've never met them

DISCOVER YOUR RATING ON THE NEXT PAGE!

Friendship *quiz*

How did you do?

Mostly As

You and your friend are two of a kind and will be best friends for life!

Mostly Bs

You're great pals but you like to hang out with other friends too.

Mostly Cs

Hmmm, sounds like you're good friends but not best friends.

JOJO LOVES HAVING HER FRIENDS JOIN HER ON HER YOUTUBE CHANNEL

Odd unicorn out

Which one of these unicorns
isn't like the rest?
Can you spot the odd one out?

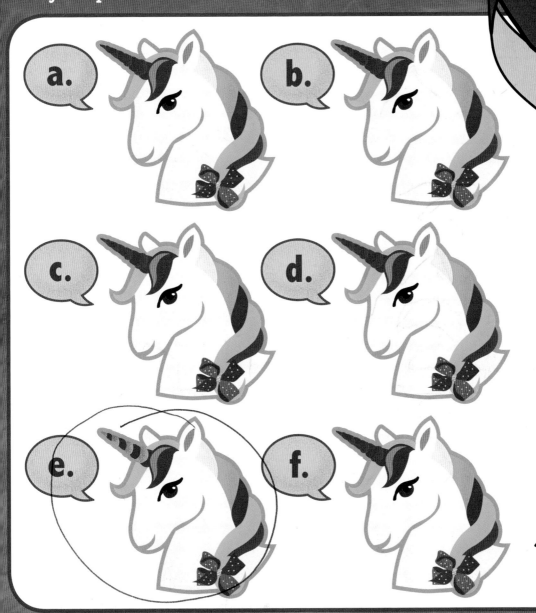

Friendship words

Tick the words below that best describe you, then ask your BFF to complete the opposite page. How do you compare?

Sweet

Confident

Happy

Funny

Sassy

Hopeful

Energetic

Dreamer

Crazy

Now ask your BFF to do the same!

Sweet

Confident

Happy

Funny

Sassy

Hopeful

Energetic

Dreamer

Crazy

25

Bow maze

Uh-oh! JoJo urgently needs to find her favourite bow for her next vlog. Can you help her track it down by finding a way through the maze?

START

FOLLOW THE RIBBON

END

CONTINUE ...

Dance search

JoJo's first passion was dance! Can you find all the dance-move related words in the grid opposite?

SPIN

HOP

TURN

LEAP

JUMP

CLAP

POINT

SHAKE

SHUFFLE

ROLL

SKIP

TAP

T	B	C	U	D	D	L	E	K	M	C	V
A	B	R	S	P	I	N	Y	R	Q	L	F
P	J	O	F	M	U	N	A	X	W	A	B
W	Z	U	W	I	T	W	L	E	A	P	S
I	F	K	M	B	M	L	Z	R	C	U	P
N	T	D	W	P	O	I	N	T	U	S	A
K	U	X	N	R	S	W	E	E	T	K	R
L	R	T	R	Y	I	A	X	J	E	I	K
E	N	G	J	P	O	C	T	H	O	P	L
J	T	S	H	A	K	E	I	G	G	L	E
F	L	U	F	F	Y	I	P	Z	H	J	P
D	F	I	S	H	U	F	F	L	E	W	I

LIVE TO DANCE

Pet poem

BowBow is just the cutest! Do you have a pet? If you do, try writing a poem about them on the opposite page. First write down 10 words that best describe them, then use them to craft your poem.

PET OR ANIMAL NAME:

BowBow

1. cute
2. Bow's
3. Mum (JoJo)
4. addorabl
5. Super pup
6. energetic
7. Sporty
8. hungry cut
9. Strong
10. anone

IF YOU DON'T HAVE A PET, DON'T WORRY! TRY WRITING ABOUT BOWBOW OR YOUR FAVOURITE ANIMAL INSTEAD!

Bow Bow Bow Bow,
How cute you are
and Mum is toto you are to adorable to
stay you are a super puppe
you are just to energetic
keep sporty
You are so hungry cute
Eat your treats
you have very strong you
have a six pack cheeky
but seein to cheeky
pup when you are alone

JoJo spotting

These small pictures of me opposite may all look the same as the big picture, but something is different in each one. Can you spot what?

Cutie cut-outs

BOWS MAKE EVERYTHING BETTER

Cut out all the cute pics on the following pages and use them to decorate your notebook, diary, bedroom or school locker.

DREAM **Crazy** BIG

©Viacom

THIS BOOK BELONGS TO:

Rose

©Viacom

THIS BOOK BELONGS TO:

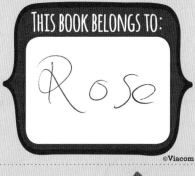

Rose

©Viacom

THIS BOOK BELONGS TO:

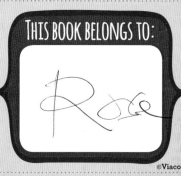

Rose

©Viacom

CUTE & CONFIDENT

©Viacom

CUTE & CONFIDENT

©Viacom

CUTE & CONFIDENT

©Viacom

THIS BOOK BELONGS TO:

Jessica

©Viacom

THIS BOOK BELONGS TO:

Jessica

©Viacom

THIS BOOK BELONGS TO:

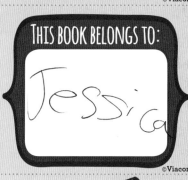

Jessica

©Viacom

Super Cute

Super Cute

Super Cute

©Viacom

✂ Please ask an adult to help you cut this page out!

Sweet tweets!

Check out these JoJo-inspired hashtags, then write your own below.

#BestiesNotBullies
#PeaceOutHaterz
#BeYourSelfie
#ICanMakeYouDance
#JoJosJuice

Bow Bow

Donuat

cupcake

Vlog

Ice-creamma

BFF

Bow your day

BOW W

~~Haters Pedd~~ Haters are Dead

....

Vlog it?

If you could have your own YouTube channel, just like JoJo, what would you vlog about? Come up with some super-awesome ideas that are important to you.

1.

Vlog idea:...

Main points to talk about:.......................................

....

Props needed:...

2.

Vlog idea:...

Main points to talk about:.......................................

....

Props needed:...

3.

Vlog idea:...

Main points to talk about:.......................................

....

Props needed:...

4.

Vlog idea:...

Main points to talk about: ....

....

Props needed:..

5.

Vlog idea:...

Main points to talk about: ....

....

Props needed:..

DID YOU KNOW THAT JOJO ENDS EVERY VLOG BY THROWING JUICE OVER HER HEAD? THAT'S WHY HER CHANNEL IS CALLED JOJO'S JUICE.

JOJO'S JUICE

Bedroom tour!

JoJo loves telling her fans all about her life – some of her favourite vlogs are bedroom tours!

I lik it

me mad it

Draw your bedroom in this frame and label your favourite parts.

Write down five awesome facts about your bedroom:

1. ....

2. ....

3. ....

4. ....

5. ....

Closet cool

What does your dream closet look like? Draw it below and organise your clothes and accessories!

DID YOU SEE JOJO'S CLOSET TOUR VLOG? #GOALS

Will you organise by colour or type?

Recipe time!

Try these easy instructions for some delicious cupcakes.

DON'T FORGET TO ASK A GROWN-UP TO TURN THE OVEN ON AND OFF!

YOU WILL NEED:

★ 100g caster sugar
★ 100g very soft butter
★ 2 large free-range eggs
★ 1 teaspoon ~~vanilla~~ chocolate extract
★ 100g self-raising flour

EAT DANCE SLEEP

1. Preheat the oven to 180°C/160°C fan/gas mark 4 and put 12 paper cases into a bun baking tray.

2. Put the sugar and very soft butter in a bowl and mix it together. Sift in the flour.

3. Crack in the eggs, add the vanilla and mix.

4. Divide the mixture between the paper cases.

5. Place in the oven for 20 minutes.

6. Take out and leave to cool. You can eat them as they are or add icing.

Cupcake crazy

Get your doodle on by adding more cute cupcakes to the page!

Who would you give these cupcakes to? Write a name next to each cupcake.

DREAM Crazy BIG

JoJo has always tried to follow her dreams and achieve her goals! She tells everyone to dream, crazy, big! In this section write down your hopes and dreams for the future.

WHY NOT TAPE THIS SECTION TOGETHER, THEN OPEN IT UP AGAIN IN THE FUTURE AND DISCOVER IF YOUR DREAMS CAME TRUE?

49

Daydreamer

school

clothes

friends

holidays

celebs

food

ghosts

TV shows

movies

dancing

family

pets

50

Dream home

My dream home would be a:

mansion ✓

castle ✓

city flat

ranch

farm

yacht

caravan

beach house

My dream home would be:

next door to my BFF ✓

around the corner from where I live now

up a mountain

on a beach

on a lake

next to a river

in a forest

in the countryside

Doodle your fave daydream in this bubble.

My dream home would be in:

UK ✓

Europe ✓

Asia

Australia

North America ✓

South America ✓

Africa

Antarctica

Arctic

Dream holiday

What would your dream holiday be like?

My dream holiday would be in:

UK ♡ ✓

Europe ♡ ✓

Asia ♡

Australia ♡

North America ♡

South America ♡

Africa ♡

Antarctica ♡

Arctic ♡

I would travel by:

bike ♡

boat ♡

plane ♡ ✓

helicopter ♡ ✓

car ♡ ✓

submarine ♡

I would stay in a:

hotel ♡ ✓

caravan ♡

apartment ♡

castle ♡ ✓

I would eat:

fruit ♡

pizza ♡

ice cream ♡ ✓

sweets ♡ ✓

Dream job

I would love to work with:

animals ♡

children ♡

only my friends ♡

on my own ♡

I would love to work:

in an office ♡

in a dance studio ♡

on the beach ♡

in a garden ♡

in a shop ♡

in a vehicle ♡

in a foreign country ♡

in space ♡

in the jungle ♡

Number these jobs from 1 to 12, with 1 being the one you'd most like to do and 12 the least.

vet

astronaut

dancer

marine biologist

teacher

actor

TV presenter

firefighter

doctor

engineer

vlogger

pilot

53

Decode your dreams!

Lord voldemaurt and his snake is hunting for me. It was really scary

If you dream you are FALLING from the sky, down a hole or off a cliff, it can mean you feel out of control. Try to work out what area of your life you need to take control of, and what you can do about it.

If you dream you are FLYING, it means you feel confident and secure about your life and in control. If you dream you are flying too high, it can mean you are concerned how your success might change your life.

If you dream you are BEING CHASED, it means you have a problem in your life that you need to face up to and deal with.

WHATEVER YOUR DREAMS MIGHT MEAN, JUST REMEMBER TO DREAM BIG, JUST LIKE JOJO!

Your dream year

January
Birthday's
Rose
Isabelle

February
Great Grandad
Bob B-day

March
Birthdays
Livia's
Willow and Dan

April
Edwards.P — Baby

May
Birthday's
Grandads
(Gary)

June
Grandma's B-day

56

July

Daddy's B-day

August

Alberts B-day

September

October

Halloween

Laura's b-day

November

Jess B-day

Alice B-day

Great Grandad
Starts jnral B-day

December

X-mas

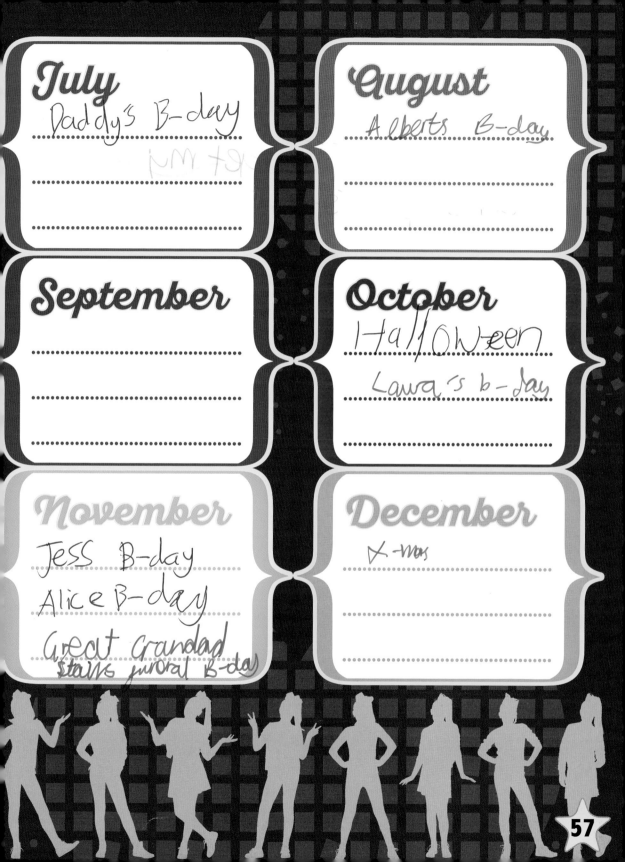

My future

In 1 year I hope: To get my ear's pearsted, Get A+

In 3 years I hope: To get A+ in everything.

In 5 years I hope: To go calafonya

In 10 years I hope: To have a baby and baby stitt eihy baby.

NOW SEAL THIS SECTION WITH TAPE AND OPEN IT AGAIN IN THE FUTURE!

59

Answers

Page 23

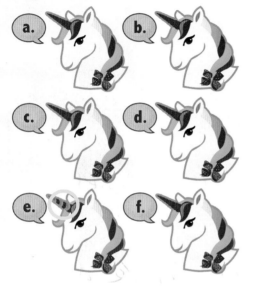

a.
b.
c.
d.
e.
f.

Pages 28–29

T	B	C	U	D	D	L	E	K	M	C	V
A	B	R	S	P	I	N	Y	R	Q	L	F
P	J	O	F	M	U	N	A	X	W	A	B
W	Z	U	W	I	T	W	L	E	A	P	S
I	F	K	M	B	M	L	Z	R	C	U	P
N	T	D	W	P	O	I	N	T	U	S	A
K	U	X	N	R	S	W	E	E	T	K	R
L	R	T	R	Y	I	A	X	J	E	I	K
E	N	G	J	P	O	C	T	H	O	P	L
J	T	S	H	A	K	E	I	G	G	L	E
F	L	U	F	F	Y	I	P	Z	H	J	P
D	F	I	S	H	U	F	F	L	E	W	I

Pages 26–27

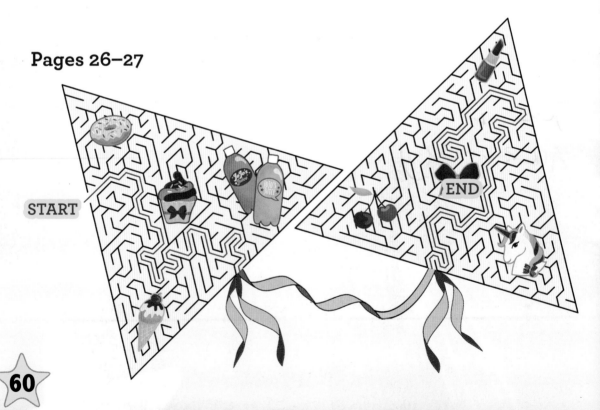

START

END

Pages 32–33

a. b. c. d.